For Kathrin
Britta

LITTLE TIGER KIDS
An imprint of the Little Tiger Group
1 Coda Studios, 189 Munster Road, London SW6 6AW
www.littletiger.co.uk • First published in Great Britain 2019
This edition published in 2020
Text by Patricia Hegarty •
A CIP Catalogue record for this book is available from the British Library
 ISBN: 978-1-78881-629-8
Printed in China • LTK/1800/0828/1019
2 4 6 8 10 9 7 5 3 1

SEA

Illustrated by
Britta Teckentrup

Gleaming and sparkling, the coral sea
Is a place of magical mystery.

As the ocean's tides ebb and flow,
A secret world lies deep below.

A small fish swims among the weeds,
They provide the shelter that he needs.

As sponges glow and grasses sway,
The fish continues on his way.

Two tiny sea horses, tail to tail,
Float along on a bubbly trail.

They may be small and very slow,
But calmly, gracefully, on they go.

A baby dolphin swims with her mother,
They leap and dive around each other.

Communicating with chirps and clicks,
They perform their acrobatic tricks.

Lionfish swims through the sea with pride,
With his feathery fins, he cannot hide.

But his secret weapon when under attack –
The poisonous spines along his back!

Suddenly there's a ripple of fear
As the fish sense danger very near.

A shadow lurking in the dark –
All fish fear the great white shark.

But nature is smarter than you think –
The puffer fish bloats, the squid squirts ink.

Small fish dart in every direction,
Some use camouflage as their protection.

As the ocean sparkles in the sun,
The tropical fish swim on as one.

Together they can find a way
To keep the predators at bay.

Rippling, gleaming, through the night,
The ocean sparkles with magical light.

Jellyfish, eels and manta ray
Dance in a colourful display.

The humpback whale is the ocean king,
The fish pause briefly to hear him sing.

The ocean fills with an enchanting sound,
As the whale's song echoes for miles around.

The little fish swim by a manatee –
The strangest creature in the sea.

In an ocean meadow, sea grasses sway,
As the sea-bed babies swim and play.

This precious coral can provide
A place for ocean life to hide.

Let's keep our oceans clean and clear
And protect our friends whose homes are here.